Violin

# WAGGON WHEELS

KATHERINE and HUGH COLLEDGE

## 1. In a garden

Count 4 bars

## 2. Summer breeze

Count 2 bars

## 3. Goldfish bowl

Count 2 bars

B.&H. 20847

2

## 4. Penny-farthing

**Count 2 bars**

## 5. Butterflies

**Count 4 bars**

## 6. Westminster Abbey

**Count 2 bars**

# 7. Dinosaurs

**Count 2 bars**

# 8. Paddle steamer

**Count 2 bars**

4

## 9. Waterfall

**Count 2 bars**

## 10. Knickerbocker glory

**Count 2 bars**

pizz.

## 11. Hills and dales

## 12. Upstairs, downstairs

## 13. Daydreaming

**Count 2 bars**

**D.C. al Fine**

11/13

## 14. Bell-ringers

**Count 2 bars**

## 19. Windscreen wipers

**Count 4 bars**

## 20. Bow ties!

**Count 4 bars**

*D.C. al Fine*

## 21. Ice dancers

**Count 4 bars**

## 22. Full moon

**Count 4 bars**

23. Waggon wheels

24. With an upbeat

# 25. On the wing

**Count 2 bars**

*mf legato*

*cresc.*

*p*

*mf*

# 26. Lollipop man

**Count 2 bars**

**Allegro**

*f*

**FINE**

*mf*

*cresc.*

***D.C. al Fine***

ISMN M-060-07947-4

Printed by
Halstan & Co. Ltd., Amersham, Bucks., England

9 790060 079474